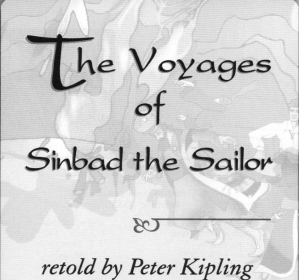

The Voyages
of
Sinbad the Sailor

retold by Peter Kipling

T0349102

Credits

First published by New Editions 2000
Reprinted 2003

New Editions
37 Bagley Wood Road
Kennington
Oxford OX1 5LY
England

New Editions
PO Box 76101
171 10 Nea Smyrni
Athens
Greece

Tel: (+30) 210 9883156   Fax: (+30) 210 9880223
E-mail: enquiries@new-editions.com
www.new-editions.com

Text, design and illustrations © New Editions 2000

ISBN   960-7609-85-9

Narrated by Tim Wilson
Recording and musical arrangements by George Flamouridis, GFS-PRO

Illustrations by Tim Wilson

Every effort has been made to trace copyright holders.
If any have been inadvertently overlooked, the publishers will be pleased to make the necessary acknowledgements at the first opportunity.

Contents

Notes on the series

The value of reading

New Editions Bestseller Readers is a series of carefully chosen classical texts, retold by modern authors in such a way that students will automatically want to read more. The aim of the series is to encourage students of English to enjoy reading for pleasure, rather than just for study. Recent research emphasises the importance of reading in helping students to learn and develop vocabulary, as well as giving them a 'feel' for the language in terms of its syntax and modes of expression.

The enjoyment factor

New Editions Bestseller Readers are illustrated, simplified readers that can be read in class or at home and have been carefully graded in terms of vocabulary, syntax, grammar and thematic content to meet the needs of students at each level. The books have been designed in such a way that students will be happy to read them because there are no signs of comprehension questions, exercises, etc. Instead, there is a simple glossary at the back of each book with an explanation in English of those words that may cause problems for some students and a separate activity book that provides students with an interesting way to understand and revise the story they are reading.

What makes New Editions Bestseller Readers special?

They contain all the necessary ingredients students need to motivate them to read:

- attractive cover design
- modern, lively, full-colour illustrations, appropriate to each level
- interesting texts
- manageable amounts of text on each page
- separate activity books
- a cassette, recorded by professionals who really know how to tell a story

Levels

There are six levels within a graded vocabulary range as shown:

- Level 1   300 words   Beginner
- Level 2   600 words   Elementary
- Level 3   1,100 words   Pre-intermediate
- Level 4   1,500 words   Intermediate
- Level 5   2,200 words   Upper Intermediate
- Level 6   3,000 words   Advanced

Students will be proud to be seen with a **New Editions Bestseller Reader**.

Notes on the Story

The Voyages of Sinbad (also known as Sindbad) *the Sailor* were originally written as part of a book of Arabic stories called *A Thousand and One Nights* (commonly known as the *Arabian Nights*).

Written in the tenth century AD, the main story was about a woman called Scheherazade who succeeds in stopping her husband killing her, by keeping him entertained with a different story for a thousand and one nights. Other famous stories included in the original work are also popular stories for young people, like *Aladdin* and *Ali Baba*.

Readers will enjoy following the adventures of Sinbad, who seems to land himself in hot water everywhere he goes.

 ## Chapter 1

Sinbad meets Sinbad!

One day a worker named Sinbad was walking along a road. His job was to carry heavy things from place to place, and he felt very tired. He needed somewhere to rest. Then he saw a big, expensive house. There were trees in front of it, and a nice bench beside the front door. So he sat down. He rested for a while, but when he stood up to leave, a servant opened the front door.

'My Master saw you sitting out here,' the servant said. 'Can you come inside? He wants to meet you.'

Sinbad agreed and went into the house. When Sinbad saw the man who owned the house, he thanked him.

'You are welcome,' the man replied. 'But, tell me now, what is your name, and what do you do?'

'My name is Sinbad the Porter,' Sinbad answered, 'and I carry things from place to place for other people.'

The man smiled. 'Well, Sinbad the Porter, my name is also Sinbad — Sinbad the Sailor. I like you because we have the same name. We are like brothers.'

'But you are very rich,' Sinbad the Porter said, 'and I'm not important at all. I'm quite poor.'

'We are all the same in God's eyes,' Sinbad the Sailor answered. 'At times, I was as poor as you are. Would you like to hear the story of my life?'

'Yes,' Sinbad the Porter answered. 'I am very curious.'

So Sinbad the Sailor began his story.

Chapter 2

The Voyage to Whale Island

My father was a merchant, but he died when I was young. I had lots of money, but I didn't know how to behave. I became very wild. I had parties every day, and they ended early in the morning. One day I woke up and realised that most of my money was gone.

'What am I going to do?' I asked myself.

I decided that I did not want to be poor. So I sold everything I had, even my house and my clothes, and became a trader. I took my goods to the port and found a place on a ship. There were lots of other traders on the ship, and we went from island to island, buying, selling and trading everywhere.

One day, the ship landed on a deserted island. We made a small camp and lit fires. Some traders cooked, while others walked around the island. I was one of the walkers. Suddenly, I heard the captain shout, 'Look out! Run for your lives! This island isn't really an island. It's a huge whale in the middle of the sea. It was asleep when we came, but the fires woke it up. In a moment it will swim under the water and we will drown. Hurry!'

When all the merchants heard the captain, they began to run. Some reached the ship, but I did not. The island shook and sank. The sea crashed on top of me, and I thought, 'I'm going to die.' But just then I saw a wooden barrel. I held on to it and floated up to the surface of the sea, but the ship was gone!

For two days I held on to the wooden barrel. The sea was rough, and the sun was very hot. Finally, at the end of the second day, the sea carried me to an island. I was weak from hunger, and I crawled onto the land. I needed food and water, but I was too tired to look for them. Soon, I fell asleep, and I didn't wake up until the next morning.

By then, I was starving. Luckily, there was a lot of fruit and fresh water nearby. After eating and drinking, I felt strong enough to look around. So I got up and began to explore the island. A few days later, I was walking along the beach when I saw a horse on a chain near the water.

'At least now I know that people live here,' I said to myself.

Soon a man came out of a hiding place. He was friendly and quite interested in me.

'How did you get here?' he asked. 'We don't very often see strangers this far away from the city.'

When I told him everything, he was amazed. 'I will take you to our King,' he said. 'He will enjoy your story very much.'

Chapter 3

Sinbad Works for the King

The king did like my story. After I finished telling it, he gave me food and showed me around his palace. He was especially proud of his horses, but I saw that none of them had saddles.

'Why don't you ride with saddles?' I asked, but the King didn't know what a saddle was. So I made one for him with the help of some of his servants. When I gave him the saddle as a present, the King was delighted.

'You are very clever, and lucky, too. I'm going to give you an important job in my city.'

The King gave me a job in the largest port on his island. Every time a ship came with merchants to buy and sell things, it was my job to write down the name of the ship and all the goods it carried. I stayed on that island for several months, until one day a familiar ship arrived.

'That's the ship I was on when I almost drowned on the whale!' I said.

The captain recognised me at once. 'Sinbad, is it really you? We thought you were dead! Oh, this is very good news. But what happened to you?'

I told the captain my story, and he nodded, saying, 'You are the luckiest man I know, Sinbad. Well, we still have all the goods you put on our ship. Do you want to come home with us?'

Of course, I said yes. But first I said goodbye to the King.

'Thank you for everything,' I told him.

'I'll miss you, Sinbad the Sailor,' the King replied. 'But you are right, it's time for you to go home.'

Chapter 4

Sinbad and the Roc

By the time I got home, I was richer than I was when I was a boy. I began living in the same way as before. But I wasn't the same person. I became restless and wanted to sail again. This time, I didn't sell my house and clothes, but I did sell many of my things. Then I found another ship and left.

Once again, the ship travelled from place to place. We bought and sold our goods everywhere we went. One day, the ship came to a lovely island. It was a very hot day, and birds sang in the trees. I was tired, so I rested for a while under a tree.

When I woke up, it was almost dark. Terrified, I ran back to the beach to look for my ship, but it was gone. Then I began to cry, and I got angry with myself for being so foolish.

'Why did I leave my nice comfortable house?' I asked.

The only good thing was that the island had lots of food and water. For the next two weeks, I continued to explore.

'I'm sure I can find a way to get off this island,' I told myself. 'I just have to be sensible.'

I searched all over the island, but without any luck. One day, I decided to climb a large hill in the centre of the island.

When I reached the top, the land became very flat. Far away, I saw a huge white dome. I walked up to it and looked for a door, but there wasn't one. I tried to climb it, but it was too slippery. So I sat down and began to think. Soon, I found the answer to my question. I looked up at the sky and saw a gigantic bird, bigger than an elephant! I knew what it was because sailors often told stories about this bird. It was called a Roc.

'So, this white dome is an egg!' I suddenly realised.

I ran away from the egg because I didn't want to make the Roc angry. Slowly it landed, covering the egg completely with its huge body, and fell asleep.

'Maybe the Roc can help me leave this island,' I thought.

So, while the bird slept, I walked quietly over to it and tied myself to its foot. I was very afraid, but I didn't have any other choice.

In the morning, the Roc woke up. It spread its wings, and flew high into the air, and I went with it. Then, after a while, it slowly began to come down again. Finally, it landed on top of another hill. I untied myself and ran away as fast as I could. Minutes later, the bird flew up in the air again. It flew very quickly, and soon I couldn't see it any more.

Chapter 5

The Valley of the Diamonds

This new hill was in the middle of a big valley with high mountains all around it. I walked along the top of the hill I was on, trying to see if there was any way for me to leave. The floor of the valley below was covered with large diamonds, but the valley was also filled with giant snakes as big as trees.

'It's hopeless!' I thought. 'Why did I leave the Roc's island? I was safe there, and I had lots of food and water. There are only giant snakes here, and I can't see any food or water anywhere.'

The snakes hid in the daytime because they were afraid of the Rocs, but when it became dark they came out. I looked for a safe place to sleep, and soon found a small cave, too small for the snakes to enter. I crawled inside and went to sleep.

The next morning, I was in a hurry. It was the safest time to go into the valley because the snakes were all asleep. So I went down, and everywhere I went I saw wonderful diamonds. Suddenly, when I got close to the mountains, a large basket fell down from the sky, almost hitting me! There was a rope tied to the basket. I looked at it for a minute.

Then I said, 'I think there is a person at the other end of this rope. He thinks he can drag the basket on the ground to get diamonds.'

I quickly filled my pockets with lots of diamonds, and then I sat down in the basket. Soon, some people began to pull the basket up. When I reached the top of the mountain I jumped out of the basket. Three men were standing in front of me, and they were very surprised.

'How did you get in our basket? Where are our diamonds?' they shouted.

'Don't worry,' I told them. 'I have lots of diamonds here. Thank you for saving my life.'

Then I gave each of the men some diamonds. The men were happy, and after they became calm they asked me to tell them my story, so I did. Then they took me to their ship, and in a week I was back home again.

'I will never go to sea again,' I said, but I was wrong.

The Ape-men

At home again I was even richer than before. For a while, I relaxed, but I didn't have as many parties as before. In fact, I was very restless. I wanted to go to sea again. After only a few months, I sold many things and got ready to sail.

The weather was very nice when our journey began, but soon a storm came. The wind blew our ship far away, and we didn't know where we were. The captain stood at the front of the ship and looked around. Finally, he saw an island.

As we came closer to the island, the captain began to look worried.

'I know that island. It's a bad place. Hairy ape-men live there, and they kill every stranger who visits. But we must go there. We need food and water.'

When we reached the island, the ape-men came out of the forest. They were very strong and very angry. They attacked the ship, but we were too afraid to fight them. Finally, the ape-men carried us off the ship onto the island. They took the ship and sailed away.

Although we were still scared, we started exploring the island and soon saw a huge building. We walked towards it, and saw that it was a palace with a wall around it, and a gate in the wall was open! This made us very happy, and we all ran inside.

There was a small park around the palace, so we slept there under the trees until sunset, but suddenly the earth began to shake, and we woke up again. The palace belonged to a giant, and he was hungry. We tried to escape, but there was nowhere to go. We were trapped!

Chapter 7

The Hungry Giant

The giant was taller than three elephants, and his teeth were big and sharp. He did not look friendly at all. He reached out his hand and held me, but then he saw that I was very skinny. He put me down again and took another merchant who was much fatter than I was. Then, before we could say a word, the giant ate him!

Every day, the giant came out of the palace at sundown. Every day he took a merchant and ate him. After three days, the captain spoke to us.

'We must do something!' he said, 'We can't just wait here for the giant to eat us!'

So we made a plan. The next morning, we went to the beach and made a boat with some logs and we took two logs back to the palace. The rest of the day, we made the logs very sharp.

That evening, when the giant came to eat one of us, we were ready. Once again he took a merchant and ate him, but then he went to sleep. We took the two logs and pushed them into the giant's eyes. He jumped up and started shouting, but he couldn't see us so he couldn't hurt us. Then he left the castle.

'Let's go!' shouted the captain, 'Everyone go to the boat!'

At that moment, we saw two other giants coming towards us. The giant had shouted for his two brothers to come, and they started to chase us!

We ran to the beach and jumped into our boat. Luckily, the giants didn't know how to swim, but they threw rocks at us. Some of the rocks hit us, and others fell into the sea. When we escaped, only three of us were still alive. We sailed for many days, and the two men who were with me both died of hunger. Finally, after two weeks, I saw a ship. I was too thirsty to speak, so I waved my arms. The captain saw me, and soon I was safe on the ship.

When I saw the captain, I was very surprised. This was the same ship that had left me after I fell asleep on an island, but the captain didn't recognise me.

He said, 'One of the merchants who was with us disappeared. We don't know what happened to him. If you sell his goods for us, we will give you some money for your work.'

'But, Captain,' I said, 'I am Sinbad the Sailor. I am the merchant who disappeared!'

Then he realised who I was and he became very happy.

'What happened to you?' he asked.

So I told him my whole story. We travelled around the islands buying and selling for a few more weeks, and then we went home again.

Chapter 8

The Magic Food

When I got home, I relaxed as usual. I forgot all about my journeys and my suffering. One day, a group of merchants came to one of my parties. They were very excited, and talked about a trip they planned to take. I got excited, too, after listening to them. So I decided to go to sea with them. I had even more money this time, so I bought very expensive goods to sell.

The weather was nice at first, but one day a storm came suddenly. The ship began to sink and before we knew it, we were all in the sea, and the ship was destroyed. I and a few merchants found a large piece of wood, and we took it and didn't let go. After a few days, we arrived at an island.

There were lots of people on this island, and they seemed very nice. There was only one strange thing about them — they weren't wearing any clothes! They found us on the beach and took us to their king. When he saw us, the king told us to sit down and eat. The food didn't look very good to me, but the other merchants were very hungry. They began to eat. As soon as they put the food in their mouths, they changed. They began to act like wild people, and they couldn't stop eating. I tried to get them to stop, but they didn't listen.

I realised that the food was magical. The people who ate it went crazy and wanted to eat all the time. The naked men ate any strangers who came to their island, so they gave them the magical food. When the visiting strangers became very fat from eating so much food, the naked men ate them. I was very lucky that I didn't eat the food!

But I was starving. I stayed very thin, so the naked men left me alone. Every day, an old man took the other merchants outside and gave them all the food they wanted. One day, I wanted to look at them so I walked along a big road until I saw the old man.

He looked at me and said, 'You are too thin to eat. Why don't you leave?'

'Where can I go?' I asked.

'Walk along this road,' he answered. 'After a week, you will reach another city where they do not eat strangers.'

So I left. Sometimes I became so hungry that I even ate grass. Finally, I reached the other city, and the people there were very nice. They took me to their king, who was amazed by my stories about my adventures. In fact, he was so pleased with them that he gave me many presents. Finally, a ship came from my own city. I thanked the king for his kindness, but I explained that I wanted to go home again. I was tired of adventures!

Chapter 9

The Rocs Get Angry

After I got home, I rested for several months. Once again, I soon forgot all my troubles at sea. I couldn't sit at home. I wanted to have adventures and make more money.

I had even more money than before. In fact, I had more money than I could ever spend. For this journey, I decided to buy my own ship. Then I found several merchants who wanted to travel with me, and we left soon after.

One day, the ship stopped at an island so that we could rest and look for food and water. While I was still on the ship, some merchants found a big white dome. They were curious, and started to throw rocks at it. Soon the dome broke, and a lot of water poured out. Then they went closer to look. Inside, they found a baby bird, but it was very big.

'The parents of this bird must be even bigger!' they said.

I walked up to the merchants and saw the broken egg.

'What did you do?' I shouted. 'Don't you know that is a Roc's egg? When the mother comes home, she is going to be very angry!'

Suddenly, the sky became dark. We looked up and saw two Rocs above us — the mother and the father — so we started to run to the ship.

When we reached it, I shouted to the Captain, 'Let's go! Hurry, or the Rocs will destroy the ship!'

We left, and soon the Rocs went away, but they came back a few minutes later. Each one held a large rock in its claws, and they wanted to drop the rocks on top of us. First, the father dropped his rock, but it missed us. Then the mother dropped her rock. This time, we weren't so lucky. The rock hit the ship, and we sank into the sea. In the water, I found a piece of wood so I sat on top of it and began to float.

Chapter 10

The Old Man of the Sea

This time, I floated for three days before I reached an island. I went to sleep on the shore because I was too tired to find food. I realised that many ships had been wrecked on that island because the beach was covered with gold and jewels. There were also lots of broken pieces of wood from the ships. But I didn't care about jewels any more. I only wanted to rest.

In the morning I looked up and saw an old man sitting beside me.

'Who are you?' I asked.

'I'm a very old man,' he said. 'Please put me on your shoulders and carry me to the trees over there. Those trees have oranges and apples and we can both get something to eat.'

I agreed, and let the old man climb onto my shoulders. Then I walked to the apple and orange trees. When we arrived, I bent down to let the old man get off my back, but he didn't move!

'Get off, please,' I said, 'I am very tired.'

But the old man still didn't move. I tried to make him get off, but he put his legs around my neck and squeezed until I felt dizzy. I couldn't do anything.

For the next few weeks, the old man made me carry him everywhere. One day, I saw some grapes. I secretly took some. Later, when the old man was sleeping on my shoulders, I squeezed the grapes into a bottle. Then I closed the bottle and left it out in the sun. Another week passed, and then I went to get the bottle. The grape juice was now wine, and I started to drink it. I soon felt dizzy and began dancing and singing, even with the old man on my shoulders.

He didn't know what wine was, so he asked me, 'What are you drinking?'

'It's called 'wine',' I answered.

'Give it to me!' he said.

I gave him the bottle and he drank the wine. In an hour, he was very drunk. He began to relax and feel sleepy. When I saw that he was not feeling well, I grabbed his legs and threw him on the ground. Then the old man woke up. He tried to look very sad and sick.

'Please pick me up again,' he said. 'Just take me to the river over there so I can drink some water. I promise I won't stay on your back.'

But I didn't believe him. So I ran away to the beach and made a raft with many broken pieces of wood. The next day I put all the gold and jewels I could find on the raft, and left the island. The sea was very calm, and in a few days I saw a ship. One of the merchants saw me on the raft, and soon I was safe on the ship. The people on the ship were very curious about me, and they wanted to know what happened.

After I told them my story they all said, 'You are very lucky. That old man is called 'The Old Man of the Sea', and he rides on top of people until they die. Then he eats them!'

They let me travel with them for a while until we reached my old city, my home.

'This time,' I said, 'I'm going to stay here where it's safe.'

Chapter 11

Sinbad's Promise

Once home, I relaxed and had big parties as usual. Thanks to the jewels from the island, I was now one of the richest men in the city. I gave my friends and family wonderful presents, and my life was very pleasant. But once again I forgot about all my troubles at sea and once again I became restless. So I packed some expensive goods and found another ship.

A few weeks after the ship left, a big storm came. The wind was very strong, and it blew us far away. When the captain of the ship finally went outside in the rain and looked around, he began to cry.

'What's the problem?' all the merchants asked him. 'Why are you so upset?'

'This is the most dangerous ocean in the world,' he answered. 'It is far away from land and filled with sea monsters. We are lost and I do not know how to get home.'

Suddenly we saw a very big whale. It was big enough to eat the ship, and it began to swim in circles around us. Then we saw an even bigger whale behind it. Finally, we saw a third whale, the biggest whale of all. It was as big as a mountain, and its mouth was as big as a valley! It swam towards us. It opened its mouth. At that moment, the wind blew even more. The whale missed us, but the wind broke the ship into little pieces.

I fell into the water and grabbed one of the pieces of wood. I was still very scared of the whales, and I was angry with myself for going on another adventure.

'Why do I always get myself into trouble?' I asked. 'Why do I go on so many adventures? I have all the money I need, so why do I do it?'

But I knew the answer.

'It's because I am greedy,' I continued. 'I always want more money. But not any more. If God saves me this time, I promise never to go on an adventure again!'

When I said those words, the wind became calmer and the whales went away. It felt like the wind was pushing me, and the next day I reached land. This place wasn't an island, but there was a big mountain in my way.

'I must cross the mountain,' I said. 'Maybe there is a city on the other side.'

The mountain was too high to climb, but I kept looking, until one day I found a small river.

Chapter 12

Sinbad Comes Home

The river went into a cave in the side of the mountain.

'If I'm lucky,' I said, 'the river will go all the way through the mountain.'

So I built a raft out of logs on the beach, and stood on it. The raft went into the cave and under the mountain. It was very dark, and I didn't know if it was night or day. In the end, the raft carried me to a large and wonderful city with many people and buildings. The people saw me and threw ropes to pull me to the shore. When I stepped off the raft, I was so tired and hungry that I fell on the ground.

Then an old man came to see why there were so many people at the river.

He saw me and said, 'Come to my house, stranger, and I will give you something to eat and drink. You can rest there until you decide what to do.'

For the next three days, he looked after me.

On the fourth day he said, 'I can tell that you are a good man. I am very old and do not have a son, but I do have a beautiful daughter. Will you marry her and become my son?'

The old man's daughter was as beautiful as the moon, so of course I agreed. The wedding was huge and everyone from the city was there. Sadly, the old man died soon after that, but my wife and I were happy together.

One day, she turned to me and said, 'I know that you want to go home. My father is dead now, so I don't mind leaving. Why don't we find a ship and go to your home together?'

In a few weeks, we sold everything that we couldn't take with us. Then we found a ship and went home. This time, I remembered my promise to God, and I never went on another adventure.

 Glossary

act (v)	behave
agree (v)	say that you will do something that somebody asks you to do
although (conj)	even if, but
amaze (v)	surprise very much
ape-man (n)	someone who is part monkey, part man
at least (phr)	whatever may happen, in any case
attack (v)	try to hurt somebody
barrel (n)	a large round thing like a box that can have water or oil in it
bench (n)	a chair in a park or garden where more than one person can sit
bend (v)	move the top part of your body nearer to the ground
calm (adj)	not angry
cave (n)	a large hole in a mountain
chain (n)	a metal rope
chase (v)	follow somebody to try to catch them
choice (n)	one out of a number of different possible things that you can take
claw (n)	a nail on a bird's foot
comfortable (adj)	nice and relaxing
completely (adv)	totally
continue (v)	do something without stopping
crawl (v)	move on your hands and knees
curious (adj)	interested in learning
delighted (adj)	very happy
deserted (adj)	where there are no people

destroy (v)	break completely
diamond (n)	an expensive white stone
disappear (v)	move so that nobody can see you
dizzy (adj)	feeling that things are going round and round
dome (n)	a round roof
drag (v)	pull along the ground
drown (v)	die in water
earth (n)	ground
enough (adj)	not needing any more
escape (v)	not be caught
especially (adv)	really, very
excited (adj)	happy that something is going to happen
expensive (adj)	costs a lot of money
explore (v)	look around a place to see what it is like
familiar (adj)	describes something or somebody you have seen many times
finally (adv)	after a long time
flat (adj)	without hills
float (v)	go to the top of the sea
forest (n)	a place where there are many trees
gate (n)	a big door in a wall
goods (pl n)	things people buy and sell
go through (phr v)	feel something, experience something
greedy (adj)	wanting too much of something
hopeless (adj)	without hope
hunger (n)	the need for food
in fact (phr)	really

jewel (n)	a stone that you find in a ring or a necklace
just (adv)	at this moment, now
kindness (n)	behaving in a friendly way to other people
log (n)	a piece of wood cut from a tree
marry (v)	take somebody to be your husband or wife
master (n)	an employer or boss
merchant (n)	a person who buys and sells things
naked (adj)	not wearing any clothes
nearby (adj)	not far away
nod (v)	move your head up and down to show you understand or to say 'yes'
ocean (n)	a lot of water between countries, a big sea
pack (v)	put things in your bag before you go on holiday
plan (n)	think of the things you want to do in the future
pleasant (adj)	very nice
port (n)	place near the sea where ships come and go
porter (n)	somebody who carries your bags
pour out (v)	when water, for example, moves quickly from one place to another
raft (n)	a type of boat made from logs or barrels tied together
reach (v)	get to a place
realise (v)	discover, learn
rest (v)	stop because you are tired
restless (adj)	not able to stay in one place
rough (adj)	wild
saddle (n)	a seat that you put on a horse

sail (v)	travel on a ship or boat
seem (v)	looks like
servant (n)	a person who works in somebody's house
several (det)	a few, some
sharp (adj)	can cut you
ship (n)	a big boat
shore (n)	where the sea and the beach meet
shoulder (n)	a part of the body either side of the neck where the arm starts
sink (v)	fall to the bottom of the sea
skinny (adj)	very thin, not fat
slippery (adj)	difficult to stand on
squeeze (v)	press something hard with a part of the body, like fingers or legs
starving (adj)	very, very hungry
suffering (n)	pain or unhappiness
sunset (n)	when the sun goes to the bottom part of the sky
surface (n)	top part of something
terribly (adv)	very
terrified (adj)	very frightened, afraid
through (prep)	passing from one side to another
tie (v)	hold two things together with string or rope
towards (prep)	to
trader (n)	a person who gives things to someone and gets something for those things
trading (n)	giving things to someone and getting something for those things

trap (v)	stop somebody from moving from a place that they want to move from
trip (n)	a short journey
trouble (n)	problem
untie (v)	make a string or rope loose
upset (adj)	not happy
valley (n)	flat land between mountains
voyage (n)	a long journey
wave (v)	move your hand from one side to the other to say goodbye
weak (adj)	not strong
wedding (n)	when two people go to church to become husband and wife
whale (n)	very large animal that lives in the sea
wine (n)	drink made from the juice of grapes
without (prep)	not having
wooden (adj)	made of wood
wreck (v)	damage a ship so that it breaks into pieces